# Follow
# Jo's Kite

*For Martin and Meg*

MYRIAD BOOKS LIMITED
35 Bishopsthorpe Road, London SE26 4PA

First published in 1995 by
PICCADILLY PRESS LIMITED
5 Castle Road, London NW1 8PR
www.piccadillypress.co.uk

ISBN 1 84746 168 9
EAN 978 1 84746 168 1

Designed by Lisa Nutt

With special thanks to Ole Thestrup of
Apostrof for all his help and support

Printed in China

# Follow Jo's Kite

## Belinda Evans

MYRIAD BOOKS LIMITED

For her birthday Jo got a fantastic blue
and yellow kite.

She loved it and couldn't wait to fly it.
'Can I take it up to the big hill after
lunch?' asked Jo.
'Perhaps,' said Dad.
But that afternoon it was very windy.
Mum said maybe it was too windy for
 kite flying.
'Oh pleeeeea-se!' begged Jo. 'It isn't too
    windy. It's perfect for kite flying.'
    'Well all right,' said Mum.

So, a bit later Jo, her little sister Meg,
her friend George, his big sister Rosie
(who promised she'd have them all
back safe and sound), and Jack the
dog, went out to fly the new kite.
'Look after Meg,' called Mum. 'You
know how she wanders.'

George, who took his collecting bag everywhere 'just in case' stopped to look in the builder's skip. 'Come on,' said Jo impatiently. 'We've got to get moving. This kite is tugging a lot - it wants to fly properly.' 'Oh dear,' said Rosie. 'Meg has wandered already.'

They hurried down the road and out into the High Street which was bustling with Saturday shoppers. 'Quick. There's our bus,' Jo called to the others. 'Cross at the lights,' yelled Rosie. 'Hold my hand, Meg.' But Meg had vanished.

They got off the bus at the hill. There were kites everywhere.
'Come on,' said Jo excitedly and began running up the hill.
'Hang on,' said Rosie. 'Wait for Meg.'

13

The wind was at its strongest as they reached the top of the hill. 'At last,' gasped Jo, and started to unravel the kite's string...

...but she wasn't holding tightly enough. 'Oh no!' wailed Jo. 'Quick, we must catch it.'

The kite was blown over the hill, down a leafy
bank and into the churchyard.
'Oh, sorry,' said Jo. 'I'm trying to catch my kite.'
'Meg,' called Rosie, 'do try to keep up.'

'Look, it's over there,' Jo shouted as they stumbled into a bring and buy sale.
'I don't believe it,' wailed Rosie. 'Meg was here a minute ago.'

The kite headed straight for the sea front
where a big parade was going past.
'Excuse me, I must get through,' said Jo.
'All these people,' sighed Rosie.
'Keep close Meg.' But it was too late...

'The kite's flying towards the pier.' Jo was
in despair.
'Oh wait,' puffed Rosie. 'I've got a stitch -
and I can't see Meg.'

'Can you reach my kite?' Jo asked the man on stilts.
'Four candyfloss, please,' Rosie said to the lady at
the kiosk.'I think we need them after all that
running. Meg's bound to turn up when she sees
us eating these.'

The man on stilts handed George his balloons and reached up towards the kite.

He leant further ...

...and further...

...and further and
then he unhooked
Jo's kite... wobbled
in the wind...

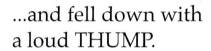

...and fell down with
a loud THUMP.

They watched as the kite grew smaller and smaller.
It had begun to rain. Jo sighed. 'I think we should
go home,' said Rosie.

'Oh dear - poor, bedraggled
things,' said Mum when
she opened the door.

Even with hot chocolate
inside them, they felt
gloomy.
'My poor kite,' said Jo.
'I have an idea,' said
George.

So they glued, painted and cut...

...and the next day they went back to the hill.

'This is the best ever kite,' smiled Jo.

Turn to the page number given with each question and see if you can find the pictures shown in the circles. Can you answer all the questions?

1. Page 5. Can you find this man in the other pictures? Where does he end up?

2. Pages 6/7. How many people are wearing hats?

3. Pages 8/9. How many people have bought a bunch of flowers?

4. Pages 10/11. How many dogs can you see?

5. Pages 12/13. How many kites are there?

6. Pages 14/15. How many hats have blown off in the wind?

7. Pages 16/17. How many people are eating toffee apples?

8. Pages 18/19. How many balloons with faces are there?

9. Pages 20/21. How many people are there in or on the sea?

10. Pages 22/23. How many people have won a teddybear - and who's just lost his?

11. Page 24. Jack the dog has been stuffing himself. What has he eaten during the day?

12. Page 27. Can you still see Jo's kite once they're home?

13. Where does George find each of the bits he uses to make the kite?

Answers: 1. He ends up on the pier, as a one-man band; 2. Forty-four (including three gnomes and Meg's doll); 3. Eighteen; 4. Twenty-three; 5. Twenty-four; 6. Five; 7. Ten; 8. Forty-eight; 9. Thirty; 10. Seven - the little boy has dropped his over the side of the pier; 11. An apple, a fish, wool, a sandwich, a piece of cake, chips, ice-cream, popcorn, and candyfloss; 12. Yes, the kite is on the television; 13. Wallpaper – in the skip, newspaper - by the zebra crossing, ball of wool - on the hill (at the bottom), branches - on the hill, confetti - at the wedding, bunting - at the bring and buy sale, flags - on the pavement during the parade, shells - at the seaside, candyfloss sticks - on the pier.